GREEK
MYTHS

Anna Claybourne

W

FRANKLIN WATTS
LONDON•SYDNEY

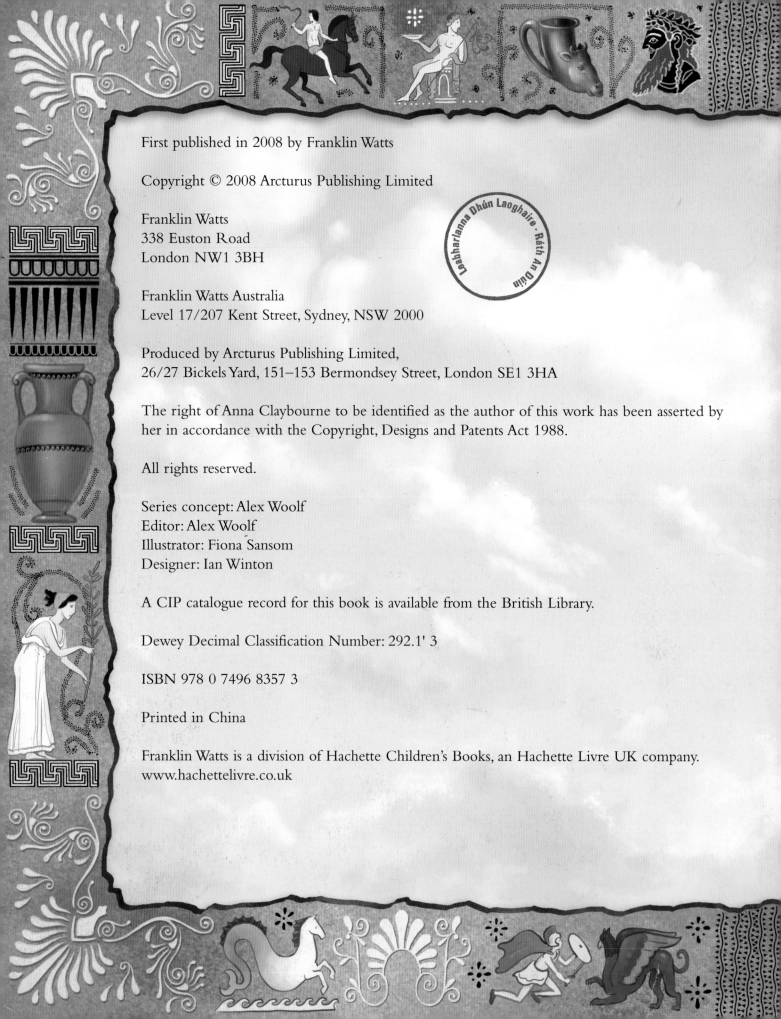

First published in 2008 by Franklin Watts

Copyright © 2008 Arcturus Publishing Limited

Franklin Watts
338 Euston Road
London NW1 3BH

Franklin Watts Australia
Level 17/207 Kent Street, Sydney, NSW 2000

Produced by Arcturus Publishing Limited,
26/27 Bickels Yard, 151–153 Bermondsey Street, London SE1 3HA

The right of Anna Claybourne to be identified as the author of this work has been asserted by her in accordance with the Copyright, Designs and Patents Act 1988.

Series concept: Alex Woolf
Editor: Alex Woolf
Illustrator: Fiona Sansom
Designer: Ian Winton

A CIP catalogue record for this book is available from the British Library.

Dewey Decimal Classification Number: 292.1' 3

ISBN 978 0 7496 8357 3

Printed in China

Franklin Watts is a division of Hachette Children's Books, an Hachette Livre UK company.
www.hachettelivre.co.uk

CONTENTS

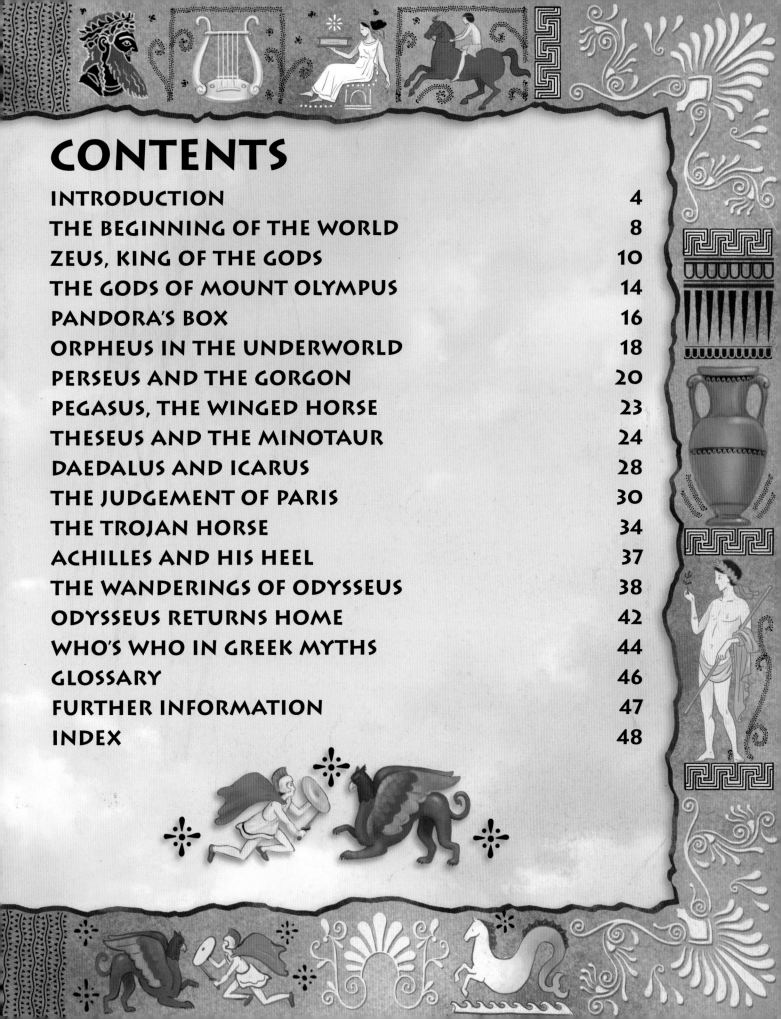

INTRODUCTION

Today, Greece is a European country at the north-eastern corner of the Mediterranean Sea. Long ago, Greece and the area around it were home to several great civilizations, which we now know as ancient Greece.

EMPIRES AND CITY-STATES

From 2000 BC, the Minoans lived in ancient Greece, ruling from the island of Crete. Then the Mycenaeans conquered Greece with their great armies. Later came the classical age, from around 600 BC, when Greece was divided into powerful city-states such as Athens, Sparta and Corinth. From about 200 BC, Greece began to lose its power, and was eventually taken over by the Romans.

MOUNT
OLYMPUS

AEGEAN
SEA

• TROY

DELPHI
•

• CHALKIS

THEBES
•

CORINTH
•

• ATHENS

OLYMPIA •

• SPARTA

N

W   E

S

CRETE

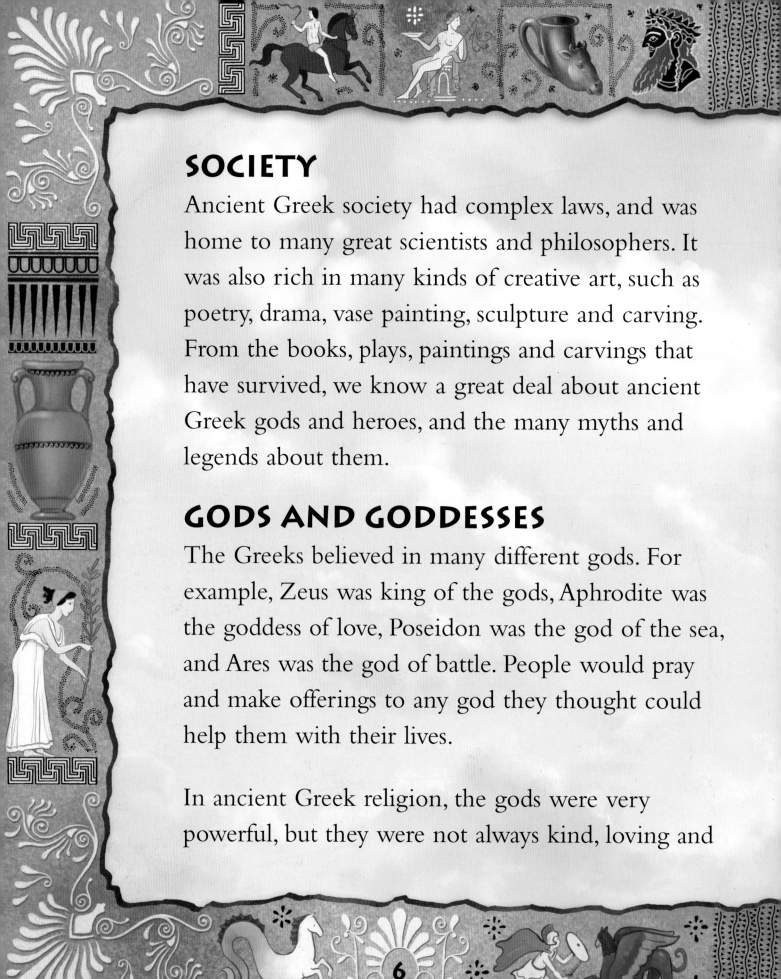

SOCIETY

Ancient Greek society had complex laws, and was home to many great scientists and philosophers. It was also rich in many kinds of creative art, such as poetry, drama, vase painting, sculpture and carving. From the books, plays, paintings and carvings that have survived, we know a great deal about ancient Greek gods and heroes, and the many myths and legends about them.

GODS AND GODDESSES

The Greeks believed in many different gods. For example, Zeus was king of the gods, Aphrodite was the goddess of love, Poseidon was the god of the sea, and Ares was the god of battle. People would pray and make offerings to any god they thought could help them with their lives.

In ancient Greek religion, the gods were very powerful, but they were not always kind, loving and caring. They had bad moods, flew into jealous rages, misbehaved and fought with each other and with humans.

BATTLES AND ADVENTURES

A lot of the stories in Greek mythology are about quarrels between the gods, and their attempts to score points against each other. There are also many other Greek myths and legends. Some tell of great heroes who fight fierce monsters and go on impossible quests. Some tell of great battles, such as the Trojan War. There are also stories of love, revenge, inventions, magic, and all kinds of amazing adventures.

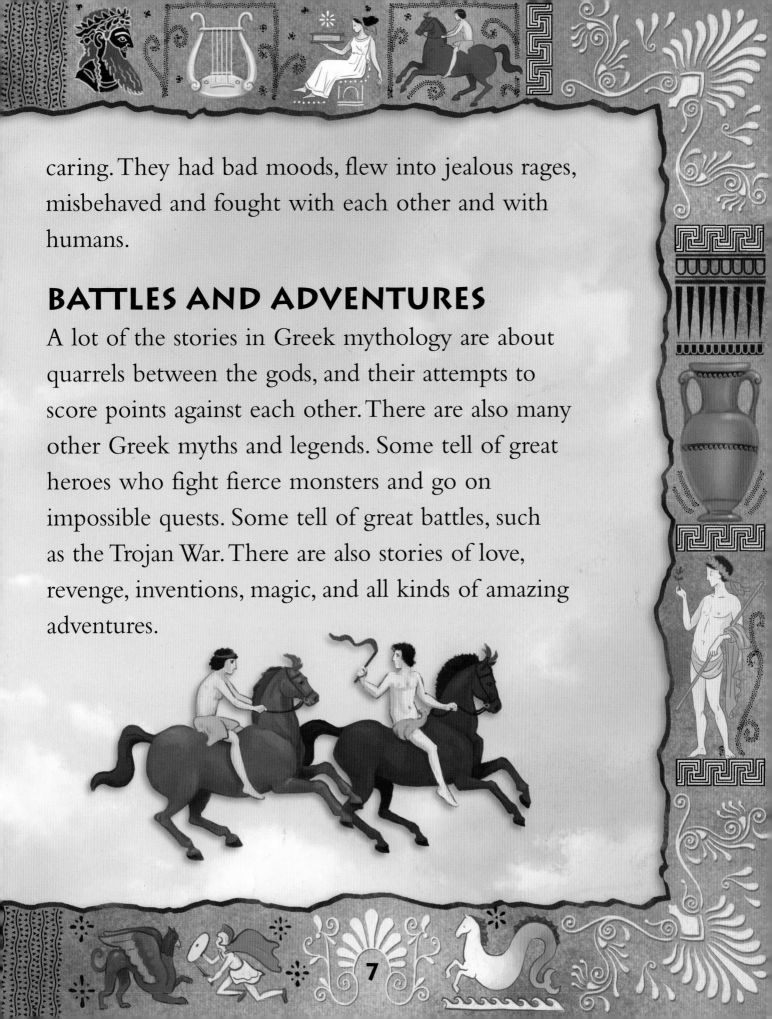

THE BEGINNING OF THE WORLD

The first gods of all were Gaia, the earth, and Uranus, the sky. Uranus was the king of the world.

Gaia and Uranus had many children. First came the twelve Titans, a tribe of mighty giants.

Their next children, however, were strange, ugly monsters. Some, called the Cyclopes, were giants with just one eye in the middle of their foreheads. Others had fifty heads and a hundred arms. Uranus hated these children. He imprisoned them in the underworld.

Gaia was furious. She loved all her children and wanted them to be free. She called to the Titans, 'Who will help me fight Uranus?'

The youngest Titan, Cronus, agreed. His mother gave him a sharp sickle, and he used it to attack his father. Uranus lost all his power, and Cronus became king. Cronus set his monstrous brothers free, and Gaia was happy. Soon, though, he changed his mind, and locked them up again.

But Gaia and Uranus could see the future. They warned Cronus: 'One day, you too will be overthrown by your child'.

ZEUS, KING OF THE GODS

Now Cronus was ruler of the world. He married another Titan, named Rhea. Their children were all great gods.

First, they had three daughters: Hestia, goddess of the hearth and home, Demeter, goddess of farming, and Hera, goddess of marriage. Then they had two sons: Hades, king of the underworld, and Poseidon, god of the sea.

But Cronus remembered what his parents had said – that one day his own child would overthrow him. He wanted to make sure that couldn't happen. So, as soon as his children were born, he swallowed them whole!

Poor Rhea wept many tears over her lost children. When she was about to have another baby, she asked the great gods Gaia and Uranus to help her. They came up with a plan to help her trick Cronus.

Rhea sneaked away to the island of Crete, where Cronus could not find her. There she had her baby, a son named Zeus. Rhea wrapped Zeus up and left him hidden in a cave.

'Where is the baby!?' roared Cronus. 'Bring it to me now!'

But Rhea wrapped up a stone to look just like a baby and gave that to Cronus instead. With one gulp he swallowed it down. He didn't even notice that he had been tricked.

When Zeus grew up, he vowed to free his brothers and sisters from his father's stomach. He asked Metis, a wise Titan, to help him. She gave Cronus a magic herb that made him vomit!

First, out came the stone, wrapped in baby's clothes. Then Cronus threw up his other children, Poseidon, Hades, Hera, Demeter and Hestia. They all joined with Zeus to fight Cronus.

The Cyclopes, whom Cronus had kept
prisoner, gave Zeus thunder and
lightning to use as weapons.
Cronus could not fight
their power, and
Zeus and his
brothers and sisters
won the battle. Zeus
became ruler of the
world and king of all
the gods.

THE GODS OF MOUNT OLYMPUS

After Zeus became king of the gods, he and his brothers and sisters went to live at the top of a high mountain, Mount Olympus.

Here the gods lived in beautiful palaces and spent their days feasting and listening to music. They ate a sweet food called ambrosia and drank nectar, which tasted like honey. The gods had many children, and some of the children also became gods.

Zeus's sons were Hermes, god of travel, Dionysus, god of wine, and Apollo, god of the sun, medicine, and music. Athena, goddess of wisdom and war, was Zeus's daughter.

Zeus married his sister Hera. Their sons were Ares, god of battle, and Hephaestus the blacksmith, god of fire and metalwork. Zeus and Hera also had a daughter, Hebe, goddess of youth.

Demeter, goddess of farming, had a daughter named Persephone. She married Hades and became queen of the underworld. And Aphrodite, the goddess of love, was born from the sea foam.

PANDORA'S BOX

Prometheus, one of the Titans, wanted to help humans. So, one day, he stole some fire and gave it to them. Zeus was furious! He told Hephaestus, blacksmith of the gods, to make a woman from clay, the first woman ever.

Zeus gave the woman, whose name was Pandora, a box filled with troubles: pain, sickness, jealousy and every kind of misery.

'Never ever open this box to see what's inside,' he warned her.

Zeus sent Pandora to live on earth. Soon she began to wonder what was in the box. 'Zeus gave it to me,' she thought, 'so it can't be all that bad!' She opened the box.

Out flew all the troubles – the pain, jealousy, misery and disease. They spread across the earth in an instant. And so, from that day to this, they have made humans unhappy.

Just one thing was left in the box – hope. Zeus had sent it to help the humans in their suffering.

ORPHEUS IN THE UNDERWORLD

Orpheus, king of the Ciconians, was taught to play the lyre by the god Apollo. When Orpheus played, wild animals became tame, and even the trees stopped to listen.

Orpheus fell in love with Eurydice, a beautiful nymph. At their wedding, Orpheus played his lyre, and Eurydice danced barefoot in the grass. But as she danced, a snake bit her ankle, and Eurydice died. Like all who die, she went to the underworld to live with Hades and his wife, Persephone.

Orpheus loved Eurydice so much, he decided to go to the underworld to fetch her back. He played such sad songs on his lyre that

Persephone wept with pity. She begged Hades
to let Eurydice go home.

'Very well,' said Hades. 'But as Eurydice
follows Orpheus out of the
underworld, he must
not turn to look
at her.'

Orpheus
agreed. But
as they left, he
could not resist
turning just once
to look at Eurydice.
And so Hades took
her back to the
underworld forever.

PERSEUS AND THE GORGON

Perseus was a brave hero. His father was Zeus, king of the gods, and his mother was a human woman called Danae.

Danae's father Acrisius had heard that, one day, his own grandson would kill him. So he cast Danae and Perseus out to sea, locked inside a wooden box. They floated to the island of Seriphus, where King Polydectes rescued them.

King Polydectes fell in love with Danae, but he hated Perseus. So he sent Perseus to fetch the head of Medusa, hoping he would never return. Medusa was one of the three gorgons, hideous monsters with wild snakes for hair. Anyone who looked at them would turn to stone.

The gods helped Perseus with his task. Hermes gave him a sharp sickle, Athena gave him a polished shield and Hades gave him a helmet that made him invisible.

Then Perseus visited the Graeae, three old sisters who had just one eye and one tooth to share among them.

Perseus grabbed the tooth and the eye and would not give them back until the Graeae agreed to tell him how to find the cave where Medusa lived.

Wearing his invisibility helmet, Perseus crept into the cave. To make sure he did not look at Medusa and turn to stone, Perseus used his shining shield as a mirror, and looked at Medusa's reflection instead. Then he used his sharp sickle to slice off her head. He bundled the head into a leather bag and proudly carried it home.

PEGASUS, THE WINGED HORSE

When Perseus cut off Medusa's head, Pegasus, a winged horse, sprang out of her neck. He leapt to the top of Mount Helicon and stamped his hoof, and a fountain flowed from the ground.

The hero, Bellerophon, caught Pegasus. He tried to ride him to the top of Mount Olympus. Zeus was angry, and knocked Bellerophon back down to earth. But he let Pegasus stay. When Pegasus died, Zeus turned him into a pattern of stars, which you can still see in the night sky.

THESEUS AND THE MINOTAUR

King Minos, of Crete, lived in a grand palace. Beneath the palace was a maze of dark, winding tunnels called the Labyrinth. And in the Labyrinth lived a monster, the Minotaur. It was half-human, half-bull, and it lived on human flesh.

King Minos had won a war against the people of Athens, and they had to do as he asked. So, every year, he made them send him seven boys and seven girls as food for the Minotaur.

Theseus, the son of King Aegeus of Athens, wanted to destroy the Minotaur. So, one year, he decided to join the group of young people being sent to Crete.

King Aegeus begged him not to go, but Theseus insisted. So Aegeus gave him a ship with black sails. 'If you come back alive,' he said, 'put white sails on the ship. Then, when I see the ship returning, I will know if you are safe.'

When Theseus arrived in Crete, Ariadne, the daughter of King Minos, fell in love with him. She went to Daedalus, the inventor who had built the Labyrinth, and asked him how she could help Theseus.

Daedalus told her to give Theseus a ball of string, so that he could unravel it on his way into the Labyrinth, then use it to find his way out again. Ariadne gave Theseus the string, along with a sword.

As he entered the Labyrinth, Theseus carefully unwound the string. He found the Minotaur in the farthest corner of the deepest, darkest tunnel, and killed it with his sword. Then he used the string to find his way out, and led all the children to safety.

But in his excitement to return home, Theseus forgot to put up white sails on his ship. Watching from the cliffs, Aegeus saw the black sails and thought his son was dead. Filled with sorrow, he threw himself from the cliffs into the sea and drowned. Theseus himself became the new king of Athens.

DAEDALUS AND ICARUS

King Minos was furious when he discovered that Daedalus had helped Theseus escape from the Labyrinth. As a punishment, he sent Daedalus and his son Icarus to live in the Labyrinth.

But Daedalus had a plan to escape. He made two pairs of wings out of string, wax and feathers – one for himself and one for Icarus.

They put their wings on and prepared to fly away. But first Daedalus warned his son: 'Don't fly too high, in case the sun melts the wax.'

They took off, flapping and soaring through the sky, away from Crete and King Minos. But Icarus forgot his father's warning. Up, up he flew, closer and closer to the sun.

As Daedalus had
feared, the wax on
Icarus's wings began
to melt. The feathers fell
apart, and Icarus tumbled down
into the sea and died. To this day,
the sea where he fell is called the Icarian
Sea, and the island nearby is named Icaria.

THE JUDGEMENT OF PARIS

When the goddess Thetis and the human king Peleus got married, they made a big mistake. They forgot to invite Eris, the bad-tempered goddess of arguments. She decided to come to the wedding feast anyway, to cause trouble.

When Eris arrived, she rolled something round and shiny across the floor. The guests picked it up and saw that it was an apple made of gold. Carved into it were the words, 'For the Fairest'.

Of course, this immediately caused an argument. Hera, the goddess of marriage, said she was the fairest, or most beautiful, of them all. Athena, goddess of war, was sure she was the prettiest. But Aphrodite, goddess of love, was outraged. 'I am the fairest, not either of you!' she fumed.

They asked Zeus to choose between them, but he refused. Instead, he asked a human, Paris, the son of King Priam of Troy, to judge who he thought was the fairest of the three goddesses.

All the goddesses bathed and put on their finest clothes, ready for Paris to make his choice. They were all so desperate to win that each goddess promised Paris a prize if he would choose her. Athena offered him success in war, and Hera offered him riches.

But Aphrodite said that if he chose her, he could have the most beautiful woman in the world as his wife. Paris liked the thought of that, so he picked Aphrodite.

The most beautiful woman in the world was Helen, the wife of King Menelaus of Sparta. But Paris did not care that she was married. He fell in love with Helen and ran away with her to Troy.

This was the start of a long, terrible conflict, the Trojan War. Kings and soldiers from all over Greece joined together to sail across the sea and lay siege to Troy. They vowed they would not leave until they had destroyed the city and returned Helen to her rightful husband.

THE TROJAN HORSE

For many years, the Greeks besieged the city of Troy. Their armies tried again and again to break in. But Troy's walls were so high and strong, it held fast.

At last, Odysseus, king of the Greek island of Ithaca, had an idea. 'If we cannot conquer the Trojans by force, we must trick them,' he said.

His plan was to build a huge, hollow wooden horse on wheels. The Greeks would hide a troop of soldiers inside it and leave it at the gates of Troy. Then they would sail away over the horizon.

'We'll tell the Trojans we've gone back to Greece,' said Odysseus. 'And when they take the horse into Troy, our army will be able to attack!'

And so the giant horse was built. By night, the soldiers climbed inside, and the Greek ships sailed away. Just one man, Sinon, was left behind.

In the morning, the Trojans were astonished to find the wooden horse at their gates.

'The Greeks have gone home,' Sinon explained. 'They left you this horse, as an offering to the great goddess Athena.'

The Trojans were delighted. They wheeled the horse through the gates. Then they celebrated with a huge party. They had won the war and got rid of the Greeks!

But as the Trojans slept, the soldiers climbed out of the horse and opened the gates of Troy. The rest of the Greeks sailed back, and streamed inside. Then they ransacked Troy, reducing it to ruins.

ACHILLES AND HIS HEEL

Achilles was Greece's greatest soldier. He was the son of the goddess Thetis and the human Peleus, so he was half-god and half-human. This meant that he could die, unlike the true gods, who live forever.

To protect him from danger, his mother Thetis dipped him in the magical River Styx. But she held him by his heel, so this part of his body was not safe.

Achilles fought in the Greek army at Troy and helped to destroy the city. But Paris, prince of Troy, fired a poisoned arrow at him. It struck him in the heel, and Achilles died.

THE WANDERINGS OF ODYSSEUS

After the Trojan War, Odysseus, king of Ithaca, set off to return to his wife Penelope and their son Telemachus.

Little did he know it would take him ten whole years to get home. He wandered the seas, beset by storms and troubled by whirlpools, witches, and monsters.

Soon, Odysseus and his men came to the home of a Cyclops, a giant with one eye in the middle of his forehead. While the Cyclops was out, they crept into his cave to steal some food. But the Cyclops returned, trapped them inside and began to eat them!

Odysseus gave the Cyclops some wine to make him sleep. Then he and his men gouged out his single eye with a sharpened log. Once he was blind, they made their escape.

Later, they came to an island where the witch Circe lived. She warned Odysseus that he would face more dangers on his way home, and told him how to survive.

First, Odysseus had to sail past the Sirens, evil women whose singing lured sailors to their deaths. Odysseus made his men block their ears with wax and told them to tie him to the mast. They passed by safely.

Next, Odysseus had to sail between Charybdis, a deadly whirlpool, and Scylla, a six-headed monster. Following Circe's advice, he sailed closer to Scylla. She gobbled up six men, but the ship did not sink.

Then they came to the Island of the Sun, where the god Helios keeps his sheep and cows. Odysseus told his men they must not kill and eat them. But they were so hungry, they did.

Zeus was furious, and sent a thunderbolt that destroyed Odysseus's ship. All his men were drowned, and Odysseus was cast adrift. Finally, he was washed up on the island of Ogygia, where the nymph Calypso rescued him.

Calypso liked Odysseus so much, she decided to keep him prisoner. Odysseus remained on Ogygia for seven years, until eventually Zeus ordered Calypso to let him go.

ODYSSEUS RETURNS HOME

When Odysseus arrived in Ithaca, his kingdom, the goddess Athena warned him that dozens of young men had moved into his palace. Thinking Odysseus would never return from Troy, they were wooing his wife, Penelope. Each wanted to marry her and become the new king.

Odysseus went to his palace disguised as a beggar. The young men bullied and teased him. But then he beat them all at an arrow-shooting contest. Everyone was amazed, until Odysseus threw off his disguise. Assisted by his son Telemachus, Odysseus threw the young men out.

Penelope was delighted to have her husband back. 'But how can I be sure you really are Odysseus?' she asked.

To prove that he was, Odysseus described how he had built the palace around a tree, so that it grew through the bedroom. Only the real Odysseus could know this. Filled with joy, Penelope threw her arms around him, and they lived together happily for many more years.

WHO'S WHO IN GREEK MYTHS

ACHILLES

Son of the goddess Thetis and the human king Peleus, Achilles was a brave, brilliant soldier who fought on the Greek side in the Trojan War. He died after being shot in the heel by Paris.

APHRODITE

The goddess of love, born from sea foam, is proud of her great beauty and was chosen by Paris as the fairest, or most beautiful, goddess of all.

APOLLO

Apollo is the god of the sun, music and medicine, and one of the many sons of Zeus. He taught the human king Orpheus to play the lyre.

ATHENA

Goddess of wisdom and war and daughter of Zeus, Athena is famous for her beautiful, flashing, grey eyes. She helped Odysseus when he returned home after the Trojan War.

CRONUS

Cronus is a Titan (giant-god), the son of Gaia and Uranus. Helped by his mother, he attacked his father and took his power, but was overthrown by his own son, Zeus.

GAIA

The earth goddess is one of the most ancient gods of all. She is the

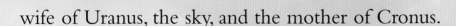

wife of Uranus, the sky, and the mother of Cronus.

HERA
Hera is Zeus's wife and the goddess of marriage.

HERMES
Hermes is a son of Zeus and god of travel and trade. He acts as a messenger of the gods.

ODYSSEUS
The king of Ithaca, who thought of using the Trojan Horse to invade Troy, Odysseus wandered for many years on his way home from the Trojan War.

PARIS
Paris was a prince of Troy who ran off with Helen, the most beautiful woman in the world, causing the Greeks to wage war against Troy.

PERSEUS
The son of Zeus and a human woman, Danae, this great hero found and beheaded the deadly gorgon, Medusa.

POSEIDON
The god of the sea, brother of Zeus, is famed for his bad temper.

THESEUS
Theseus was a hero who entered the Labyrinth of King Minos and killed the monstrous Minotaur that lived there.

ZEUS
Zeus is the king of the gods. When he was a baby, his mother Rhea hid him from his father, Cronus, who intended to swallow him. Zeus was married to Hera, and his many children included several gods and great heroes.

GLOSSARY

ambrosia A sweet food eaten by the gods.

Charybdis A deadly whirlpool that could suck ships underwater.

city-state An ancient Greek kingdom made up of a walled city and the land surrounding it.

Cyclops (plural: Cyclopes) A giant with a single eye in the middle of his forehead.

gorgon A monstrous woman with snakes for hair, whose look could turn people to stone.

Graeae Three old women who shared one eye and one tooth.

Labyrinth The underground maze where King Minos kept the Minotaur.

lyre A musical instrument similar to a small harp.

Minotaur A monster that was half-human and half-bull.

nectar A sweet honey-like drink enjoyed by the gods.

nymph A minor nature goddess.

Pegasus A winged horse, born from Medusa's neck when her head was cut off.

Scylla A man-eating, six-headed female monster with a fish's tail.

sickle A long, curved knife, used for cutting grass or as a weapon.

Sirens Beautiful female monsters that lure sailors with their haunting songs.

Titans An early race of giant gods, the children of Gaia and Uranus.

woo Try to persuade someone to marry you.

FURTHER INFORMATION

BOOKS

The Usborne Encyclopedia of Ancient Greece by Jane Chisholm, Lisa Miles and Struan Reid (Usborne Publishing, 2007)

Ancient Greece (with CD ROM) by Anne Pearson (Dorling Kindersley, 2007)

D'Aulaire's Book of Greek Myths by Ingri and Edgar Parin D'Aulaire (Delacorte Press, 2003)

Greek Myths by Marcia Williams (Walker Books, 2006)

WEBSITES

www.historyforkids.org/learn/greeks/religion/greekrelig.htm
Greek Myths – History for Kids. Entertaining versions of Greek myths and lots of useful background information.

www.bbc.co.uk/schools/ancientgreece/main_menu.shtml
BBC Schools: Ancient Greece. Fascinating facts on many aspects of ancient Greek life.

INDEX

Leabharlanna Dhún Laoghaire · Ráth An Dúin